Benny and the Biscuits

By Kathryn Harper
Illustrated by Richard Watson

Before you read, match the people with the pictures. Write the numbers. Who is this story about?

1 Benny
2 sister
3 grandpa
4 grandma
5 uncle
6 cousin

BENNY'S sister is in the kitchen.
She is making biscuits.

biscuit

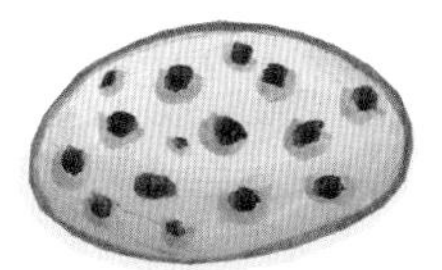

kitchen

sister

Benny comes in the kitchen. He loves biscuits.

Benny says:

'Yummm! These biscuits smell **very** good.

I'm very hungry.'

Benny is hungry.

The biscuits smell **very** good.

Benny's *favourite* place is a tree in the park.

He likes to eat biscuits there.

hungry

park

smell

tree

Benny takes a biscuit. He puts it in a bag.
He goes to the door – and he stops.
The biscuits smell **very** good.

bag

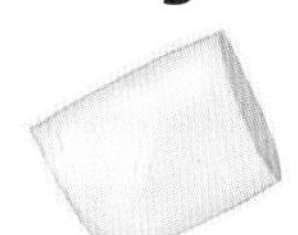

door

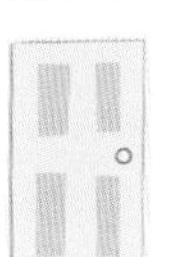

stop

Benny takes three biscuits.
He puts them in his bag.

Now he's got one, two, three, *four* biscuits.
He goes to the door – and he stops.
The biscuits smell **very** good.

one **1** two **2** three **3** four **4**

Join the dots and write the correct word.

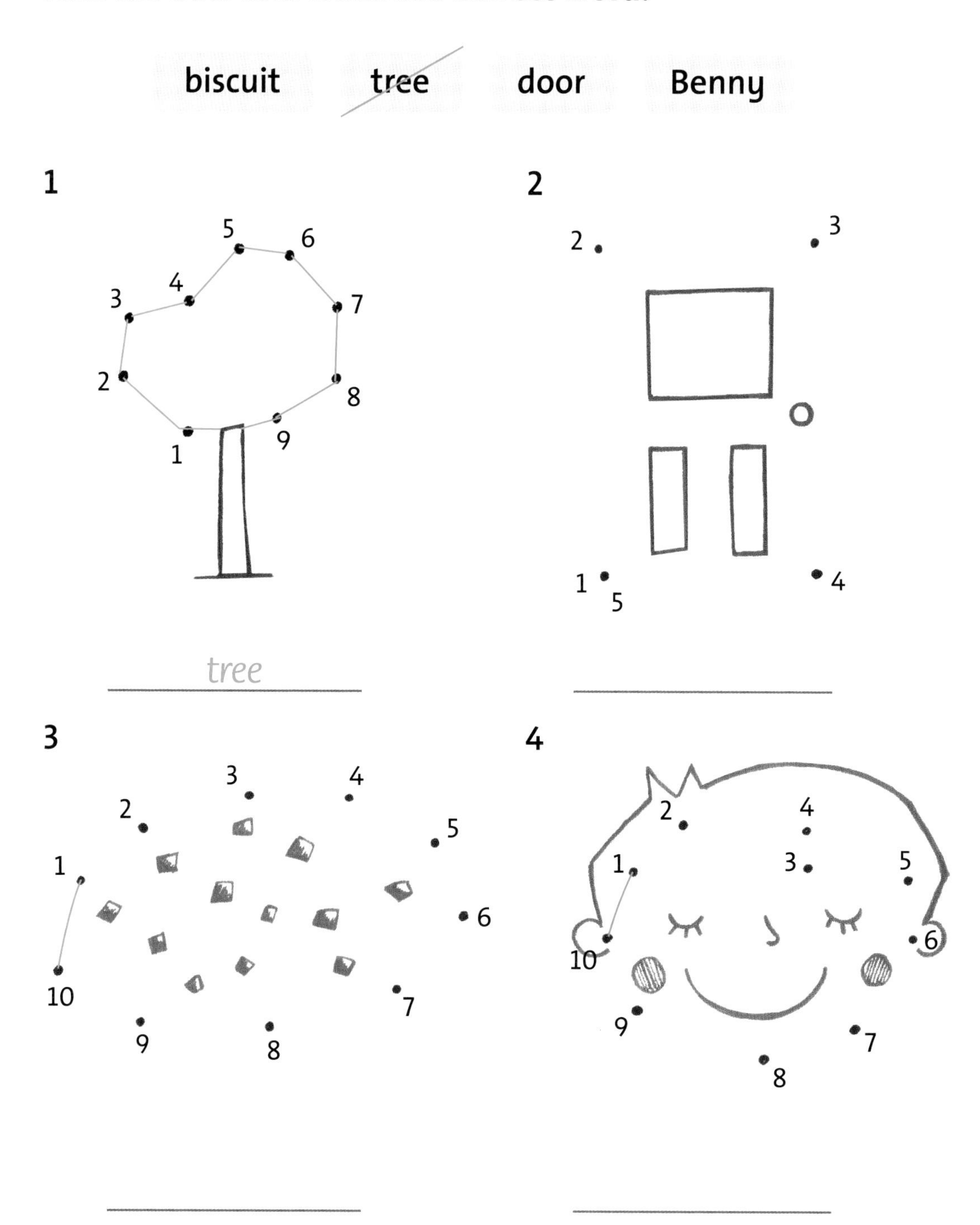

Look at the picture and count. Write the number.

1 ___four___ biscuits

2 ____________ trees

3 ____________ door

4 ____________ bags

Benny takes six biscuits.
He puts them in his bag.
Now he's got

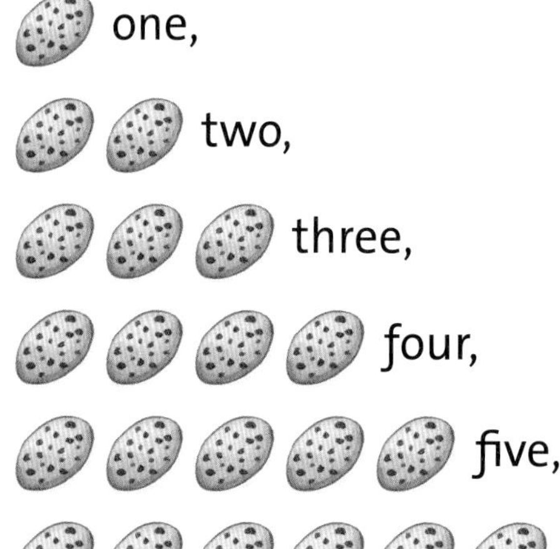

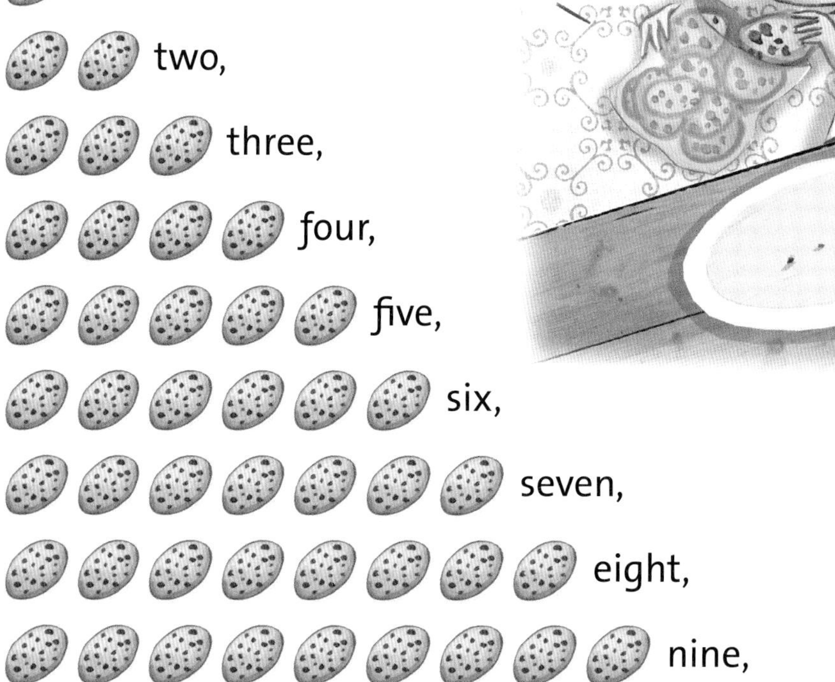

one,

two,

three,

four,

five,

six,

seven,

eight,

nine,

ten biscuits!

Benny's sister comes
in the kitchen.
Benny runs to the door.
He's got ten biscuits
in his bag.

run

Benny's sister is angry. Where are the biscuits?
She sees Benny. She says:
'Give back the biscuits!'

angry

give back

Benny runs down the road.
Benny's cousin is at the school.
She says:
'Yummm! Those biscuits smell **very** good.'
Benny's sister runs down the road. She says:
'Give back the biscuits!'

road

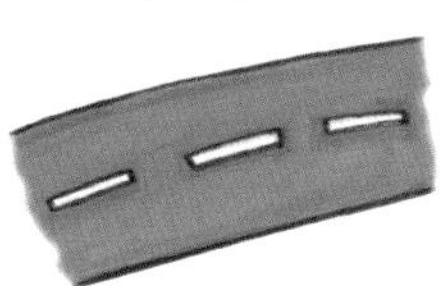

school

Benny runs down the road.
Benny's uncle is at the football field.
He says:
'Yummm! Those biscuits smell **very** good.'
His sister and his cousin say:
'Give back the biscuits!'

---

football field

Look and count. Write the numbers.

1 ___six___ biscuits

2 ________ biscuits

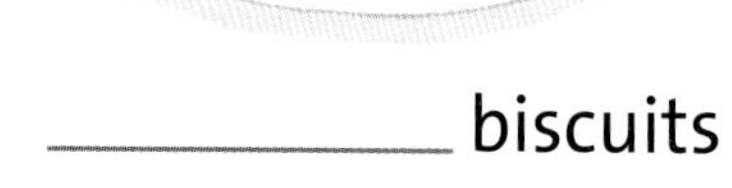

3 ________ biscuits

4 ________ biscuits

Match the pictures with the sentences.

1 Benny's sister is making biscuits. [c]

2 Benny comes in the kitchen. [ ]

3 Benny puts a biscuit in his bag. [ ]

4 Benny has got four biscuits. [ ]

Benny runs down the road.
Benny's grandma is at her house.
She says:
'Yummm! Those biscuits smell **very** good.'
His sister, his cousin and his uncle say:
'Give back the biscuits!'

grandma

house

Benny runs down the road.
His grandpa is at the bookshop.
He says:
'Yummm! Those biscuits smell **very** good.'
His sister, his cousin, his uncle and his grandma say:
'Give back the biscuits!'

---

bookshop

grandpa

Benny runs to the park.
He climbs his favourite tree.
His sister, his cousin, his uncle,
his grandma and his grandpa say:
'Give back the biscuits!'

climb

Benny is in the tree. He opens the bag. He says:
'Yummm! These biscuits smell **very** good.'

His sister, his cousin, his uncle, his grandma
and his grandpa say:
'Give back the biscuits!'
They are very noisy. The tree shakes.

---

noisy

shake

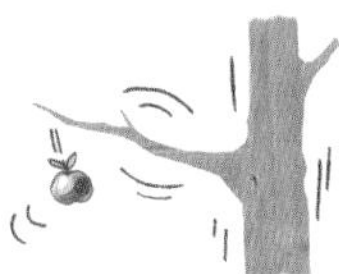

Match and write the word.

Write the words. Circle the things that are not in the story.

grandma ~~pool~~ teddy ~~house~~ sofa bag

sister baby book door ~~school~~ table

1

house

school

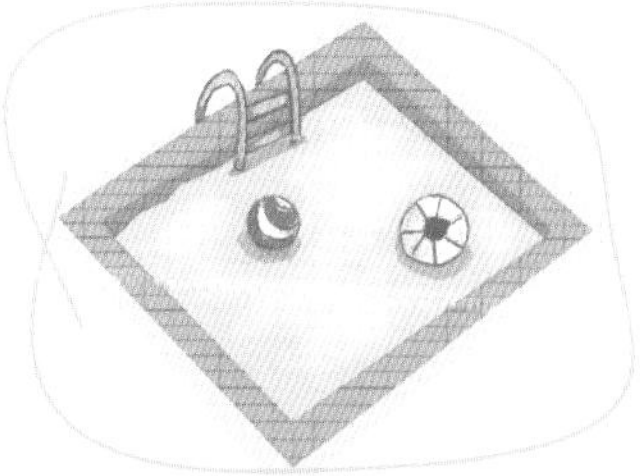

pool

2

_______ _______ _______

3

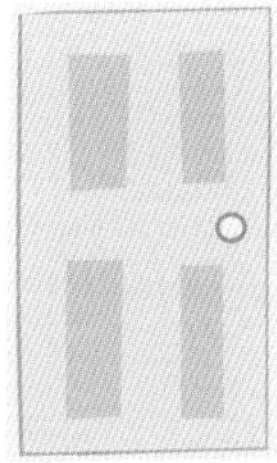

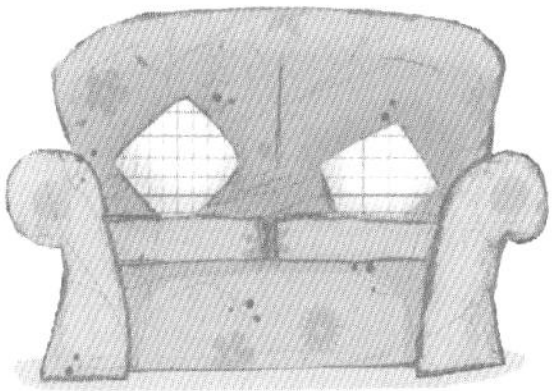

_______ _______ _______

4

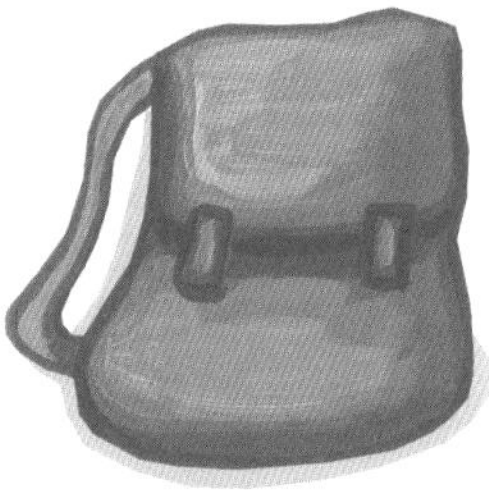

_______ _______ _______

Benny drops the biscuits.
They fall down...

Now there are only crumbs.

---

crumbs	down	drop	fall
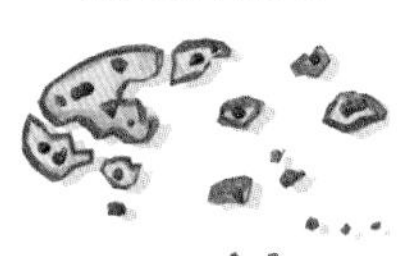			

Benny's sister is sad. She says:
'No biscuits – there are only crumbs.'
Benny climbs down the tree.

sad

Benny says:
'I'm sorry. But the biscuits smell **very** good.'

They give the crumbs to the birds.
The birds are happy. They like crumbs.

bird

Now Benny is helping his sister.
They are making biscuits.
Benny's cousin, his uncle, his grandma and his grandpa say:
'Yummm! Those biscuits smell **very** good.'

help

Number the pictures in order to tell the story.

Find and circle the words. Then write.

b	i	s	c	u	i	t	e
o	o	k	r	n	d	e	g
o	c	r	u	m	b	s	r
k	r	p	a	r	s	u	a
s	i	s	t	e	r	i	n
h	o	i	s	r	o	a	d
o	g	t	r	e	e	b	p
p	a	r	k	r	o	d	a

1 

b o o k s h o p

2 

_ _ _ _ _ _

3 

_ _ _ _

4 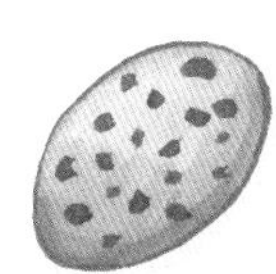

_ _ _ _ _ _ _

5 

_ _ _ _ _ _

6 

_ _ _ _ _ _ _

7 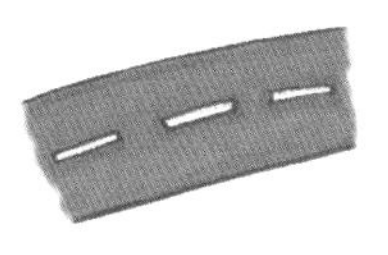

_ _ _ _

8 

_ _ _ _

Act the play.

Scene 1

Narrator Benny's sister is making biscuits.

Sister (*singing*) La, la, la. Yummm! These biscuits smell good.

Benny Yummm! Those biscuits smell **very** good. I love biscuits.

Narrator Benny is hungry. He takes a biscuit. He puts it in a bag. He goes to the door – and he stops.

Benny The biscuits smell **very** good.

Narrator Benny takes three biscuits.
He puts them in his bag.
Now he's got one, two, three, four biscuits.
He goes to the door – and he stops.

Benny The biscuits smell **very** good.

Narrator Benny takes six biscuits.
He puts them in his bag.
Now he's got one, two, three, four, five, six, seven, eight, nine, ten biscuits.

Benny The biscuits smell **very** good.

Narrator Benny's sister is coming.
Benny runs to the door.

Sister (*angrily*) Where are the biscuits?
Benny! Give back the biscuits!

Scene 2

Narrator Benny runs down the road.
His cousin is at the school.

Cousin Yummm! Those biscuits smell **very** good.

Sister **Benny! Give back the biscuits!**

Narrator Benny runs down the road.
His uncle is at the football field.

Uncle Yummm! Those biscuits smell **very** good.

Sister and cousin
Benny! Give back the biscuits!

Narrator Benny runs down the road.
His grandma is at her house.

Grandma Yummm! Those biscuits smell **very** good.

Sister, cousin and uncle
Benny! Give back the biscuits!

Narrator Benny runs down the road.
His grandpa is at the bookshop.

Grandpa Yummm. Those biscuits
smell **very** good.

Sister, cousin, uncle and grandma
Benny! Give back the biscuits!

Scene 3

Narrator Benny runs to the park.
He climbs his favourite tree.

Benny These biscuits smell **very** good.

All **Benny! Give back the biscuits!**

Narrator They are very noisy. The tree shakes.
Benny drops the biscuits.
They fall down, down, down, down.
Now there are only crumbs.

Sister (*crying*) No biscuits – there are only crumbs.

Benny I'm sorry. But the biscuits smell **very** good.

Sister Look at the birds. They are hungry.

Benny Let's give the crumbs to the birds.

Narrator The birds are happy. They like the crumbs.

Scene 4

Benny I can help you make biscuits.

All Yummm. Those biscuits smell **very** good.

OXFORD
UNIVERSITY PRESS

Great Clarendon Street, Oxford OX2 6DP

Oxford University Press is a department of the University of Oxford.
It furthers the University's objective of excellence in research, scholarship,
and education by publishing worldwide in

Oxford New York

Auckland Cape Town Dar es Salaam Hong Kong Karachi
Kuala Lumpur Madrid Melbourne Mexico City Nairobi
New Delhi Shanghai Taipei Toronto

With offices in

Argentina Austria Brazil Chile Czech Republic France Greece
Guatemala Hungary Italy Japan Poland Portugal Singapore
South Korea Switzerland Thailand Turkey Ukraine Vietnam

First published 2009
2013 2012 2011 2010 2009
10 9 8 7 6 5 4 3 2 1

ISBN: 978 0 19 480254 3

Printed in China

ACKNOWLEDGEMENTS
Story by: Kathryn Harper
Illustrated by: Richard Watson / Bright Agency